12 SAXOPHONE TRI

arranged by
HARRY GEE

CONTENTS

12 SAXOPHONE TRIOS
GREENSLEEVES

Old English Air
Arranged by Harry Gee

SHADOWS OF THE NIGHT

Old French Carol
Arranged by Harry Gee

COUNTRY DANCE

Old Russsian
Arranged by Harry Gee

RIGADOON

Henry Purcell
Arranged by Harry Gee

ADAGIO
FROM TRIO NO. 5

James Hook Op. 83
Arranged by Harry Gee

CANON

W. A. Mozart, K. 508
Arranged by Harry Gee

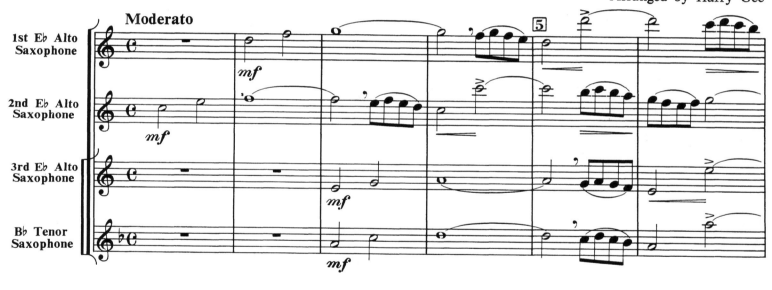

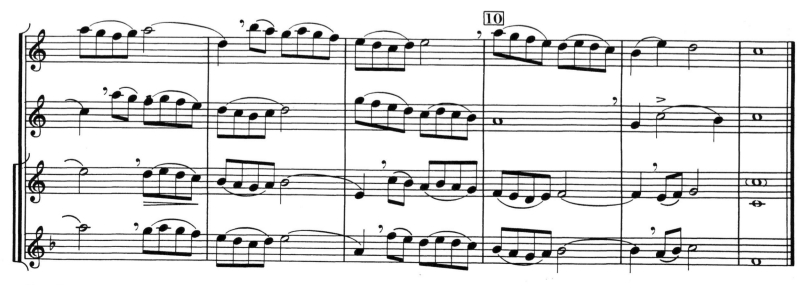

ADAGIO

Arcangelo Corelli
Arranged by Harry Gee

SARABANDE

G. F. Handel
Arranged by Harry Gee

BAGATELLE

Ludwig Van Beethoven
Arranged by Harry Gee

D.S. al Fine

DOLL'S SLUMBER SONG

Robert Schumann
Arranged by Harry Gee

MEDITATION

Harry Gee

RECREATION

Harry Gee

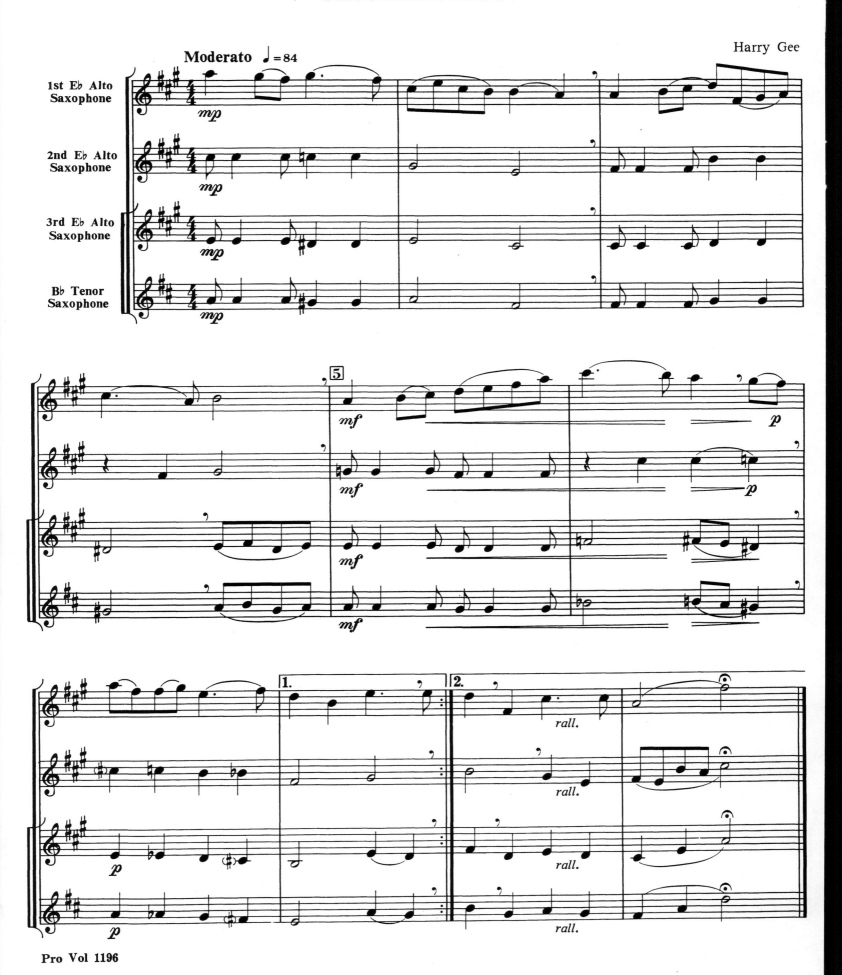